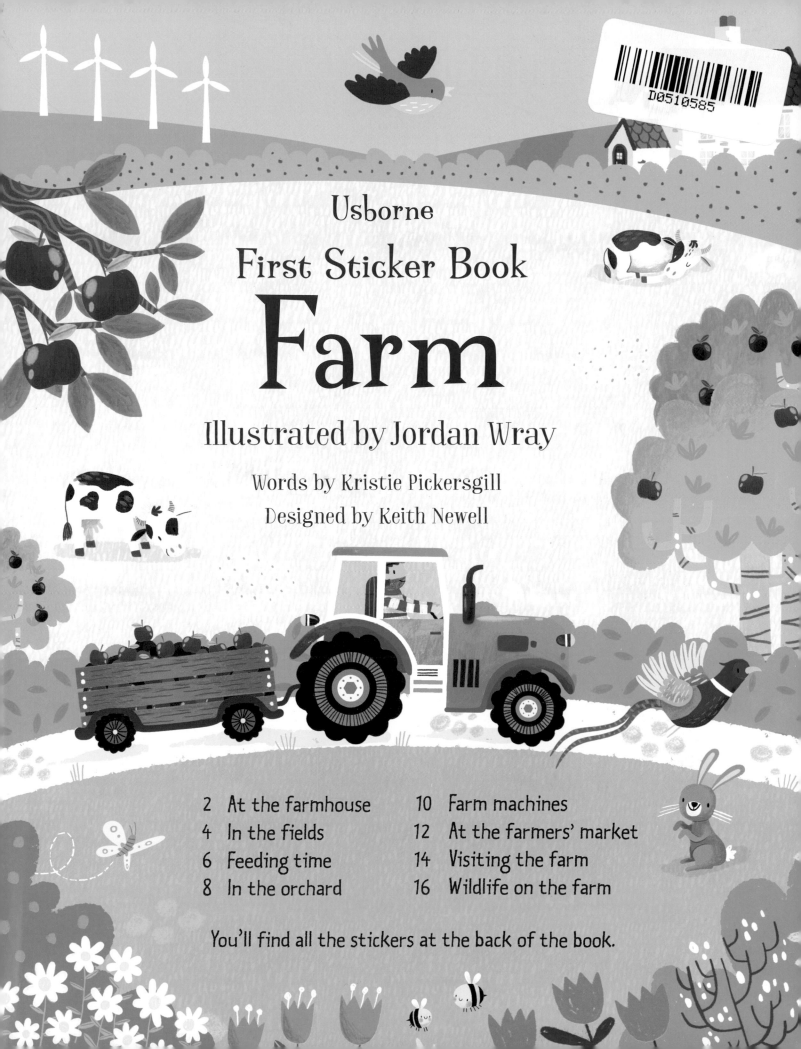

Usborne

First Sticker Book
Farm

Illustrated by Jordan Wray

Words by Kristie Pickersgill

Designed by Keith Newell

You'll find all the stickers at the back of the book.

At the farmhouse

There's lots to do on the farm today. Can you find someone to wash the muddy tractor?

Add more windows to the farmhouse.

Stick another grain silo here.

Put some eggs in the goose's nest.

3

In the fields

The farmer needs to get the sheep into their pen to shear them (cut off their wool). Can you help her?

Fill the pen with sheep and find somebody to shear them.

Feeding time

The chickens and pigs are hungry. Find a bucket of grain for the chickens and a food trough for the pigs.

Can you find someone to collect the eggs?

Add more water to the
pigs' wallow to keep it
nice and muddy.

7

In the orchard

The trees and bushes are heavy with ripe fruit.
Stick on lots of people to pick it.

Find someone to pick the
blackberries on this bush.

Add a ladder for reaching
the highest apples.

Inside the beehives there are frames
filled with honey. Find a beekeeper
to take them out.

9

Farm machines

There are lots of big machines to help farmers plant and harvest their crops. Can you add some to this page?

Add a tiller being pulled along behind the tractor.

Find a machine that
makes bales of hay.

Stick a combine harvester
in this field to cut
and sort the grain.

Put a potato planter here.

At the farmers' market

There's lots of lovely food to buy at the farmers' market. Fill the stalls with delicious things.

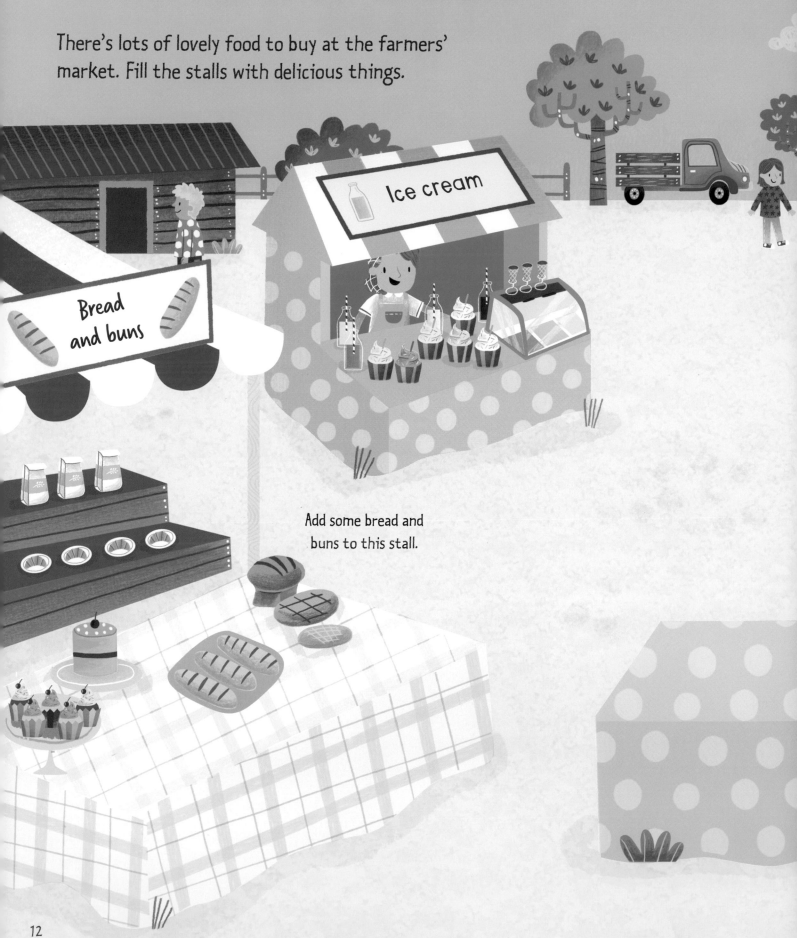

Ice cream

Bread and buns

Add some bread and buns to this stall.

Cheese

Vic's Vegetables

Potatoes

Visiting the farm

The farm is open for visitors and there are lots of animals to meet.

Llamas

Pet corner

Please wash your hands

Add some rabbits and guinea pigs to the petting area.

Add more people on the farm tour.

Hand wash

Goats

Wildlife on the farm

As the sun sets, other creatures that live around the farm come out. Add lots more animals to this page.

Add a swooping owl to the sky.

Who is looking out of the burrow?

Add a harvest mouse climbing the corn.

Feeding time pages 6-7

Chicken coop

Food trough

Pigs

In the orchard pages 8–9

Beekeeper

Farm machines pages 10–11

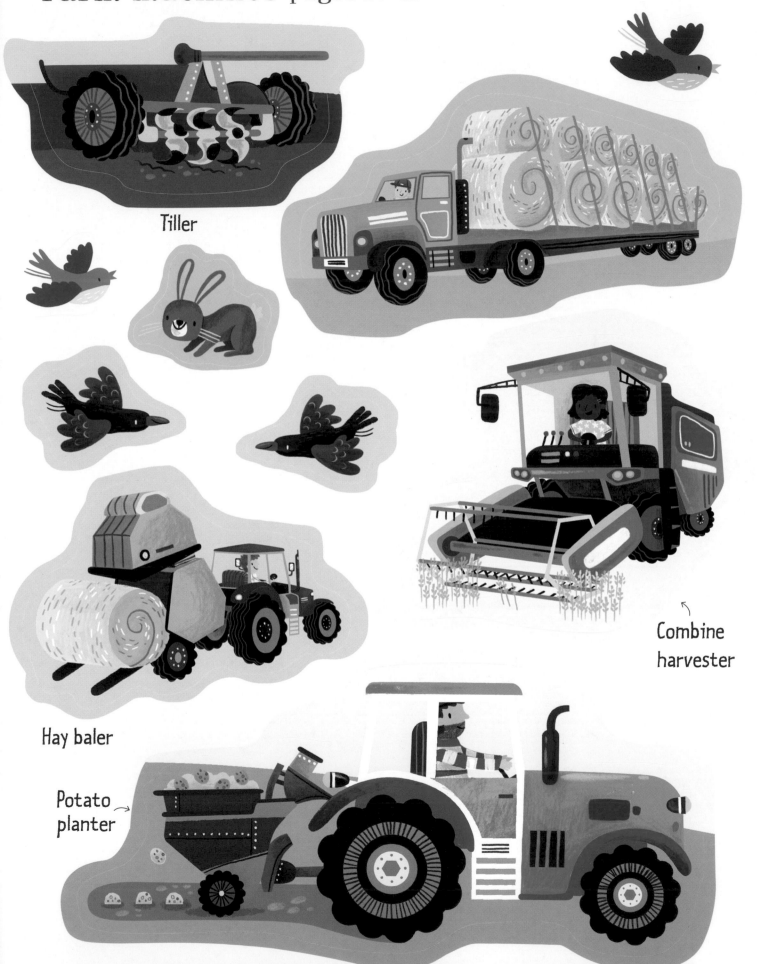

Tiller

Combine harvester

Hay baler

Potato planter

At the farmers' market pages 12–13

Buns

Onions

Bread

Visiting the farm pages 14–15

Llamas

Guinea pigs

Horse and foal

Goats

Wildlife on the farm

Owl

Pheasants

Foxes

Deer

Corn

Rabbits

Harvest mouse